▲ ART THERAPY COLORING

BUTTERFLY
COLORING BOOK
FOR ADULTS

Black Background

Preview of Coloring Pages

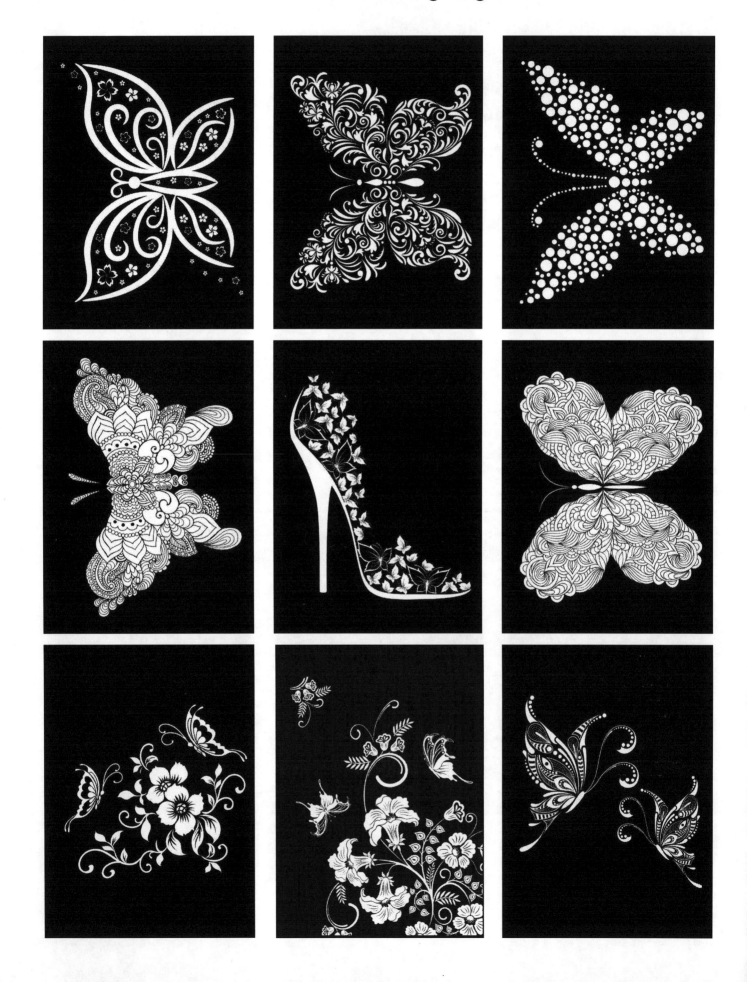

Preview of Coloring Pages

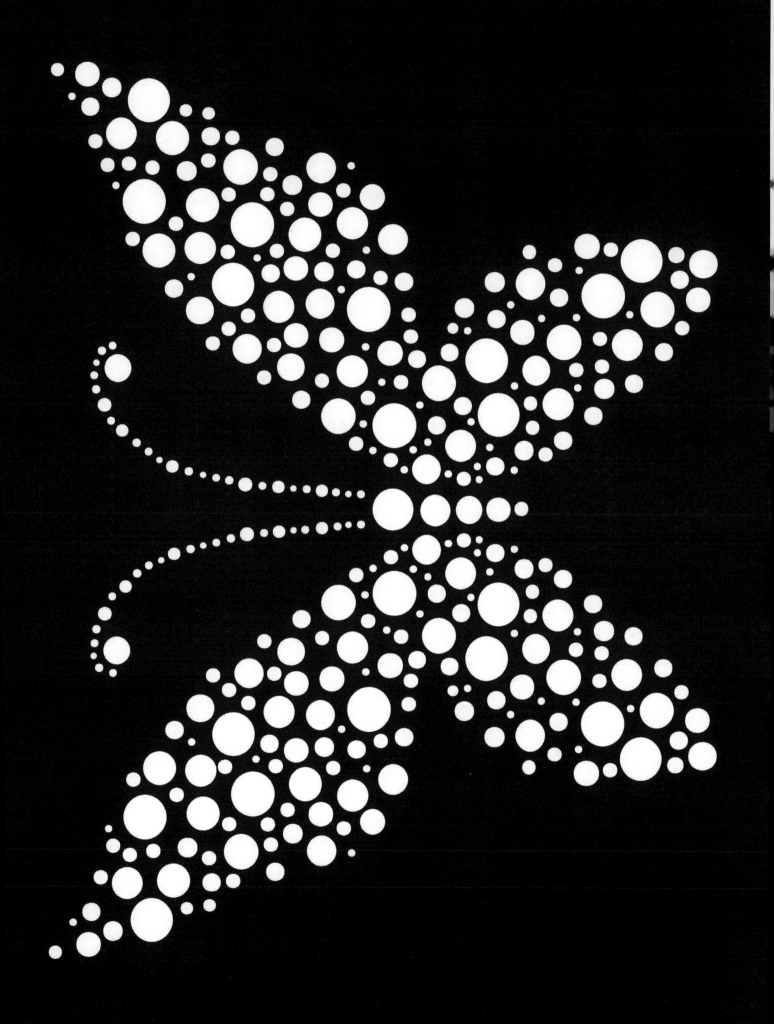

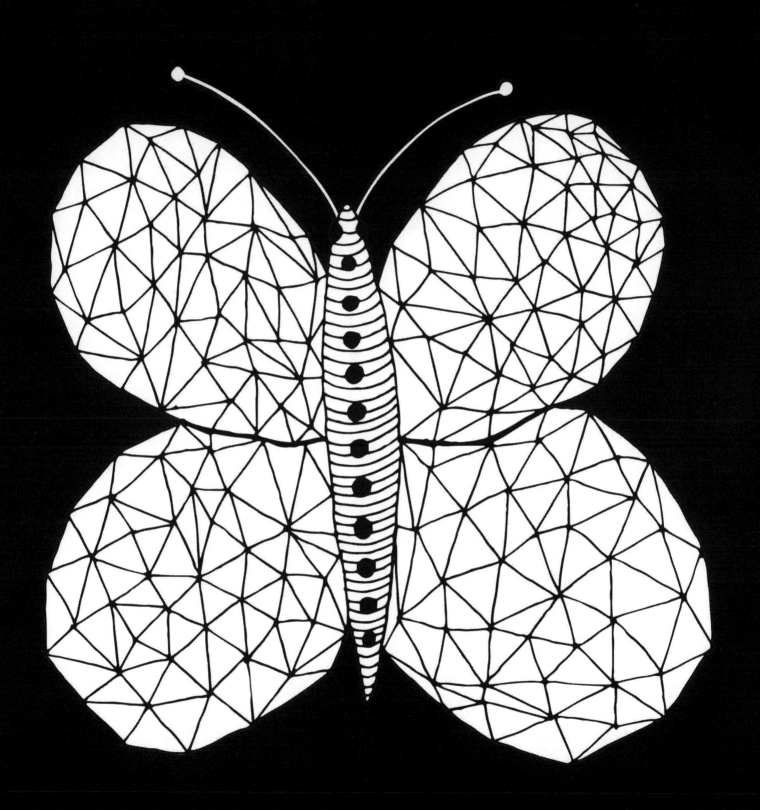

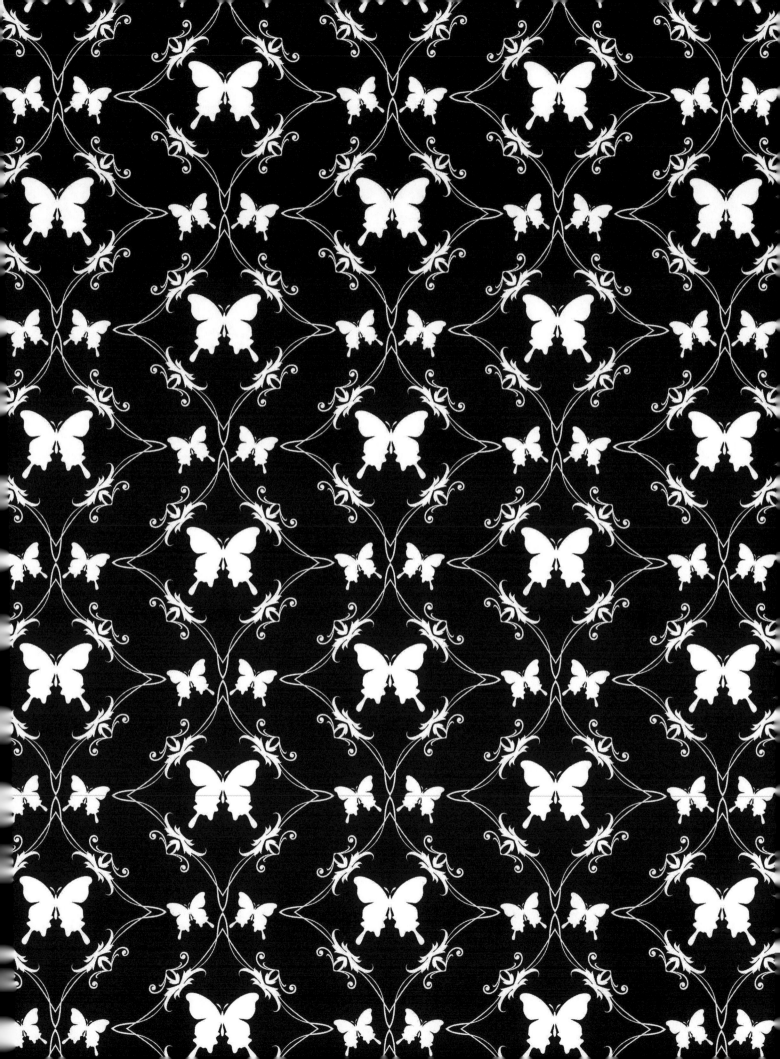

Test Your Colors

Best Selling Art Therapy Coloring Books

Coloring Books For Adults:

- Zombie Coloring Book: Black Background
- Butterfly Coloring Book For Adults: Black Background
- Tattoo Coloring Book: Black Background
- Coloring Books for Adults Relaxation: Native American Inspired Designs
- Fishing Coloring Book for Adults: Black Background

Coloring Books For Men:

- Coloring Book for Men: Anti-Stress Designs Vol 1
- Coloring Book For Men: Fishing Designs
- Coloring Book For Men: Tattoo Designs
- Coloring Books for Men: Hunting
- Coloring Book For Men: Biker Designs

Coloring Books For Seniors:

- Coloring Book For Seniors: Nature Designs Vol 1
- Coloring Book For Seniors: Anti-Stress Designs Vol 1
- Coloring Books for Seniors: Relaxing Designs
- Coloring Book For Seniors: Floral Designs Vol 1
- Coloring Book For Seniors: Ocean Designs Vol 1

Coloring Books For Teens and Tweens:

- Coloring Books For Teens: Ocean Designs
- Coloring Books for Teen Girls Vol 1
- Teen Inspirational Coloring Books
- Coloring Book for Teens: Anti-Stress Designs Vol 1
- Tween Coloring Books For Girls: Cute Animals

Coloring Books For Kids:

- Horse Coloring Book For Girls
- Coloring Books For Boys: Sharks
- Coloring Books for Boys: Animal Designs
- Unicorn Coloring Book for Girls
- Detailed Coloring Books For Kids

Coloring Books For Adults

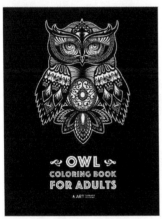

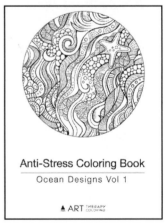

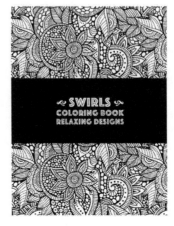

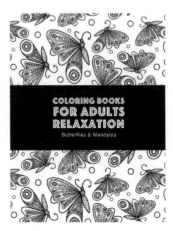

Coloring Books For Adults

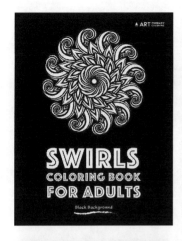

SWIRLS COLORING BOOK FOR ADULTS
Black Background

PATTERNS COLORING BOOK FOR ADULTS
Black Background

DRAGON COLORING BOOK

DRAGON COLORING BOOK
Black Background

AFRICA COLORING BOOK FOR ADULTS

LION COLORING BOOK FOR ADULTS

TIGER COLORING BOOK FOR ADULTS

WILD ANIMALS COLORING BOOK ZENDOODLE DESIGNS

UNICORN ADULT COLORING BOOKS
Black Background

HORSE COLORING BOOK DETAILED DESIGNS

HORSE COLORING BOOKS FOR ADULTS
Black Background

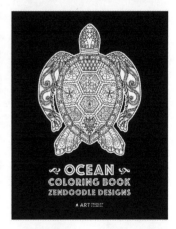

OCEAN COLORING BOOK ZENDOODLE DESIGNS

WOLF COLORING BOOK FOR ADULTS

DOG COLORING BOOK DOODLE DESIGNS

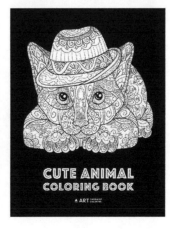

CUTE ANIMAL COLORING BOOK

CUTE CAT COLORING BOOK

Coloring Books For Teens

COLORING BOOKS
FOR TEENS
WOLVES & MORE

TEEN
COLORING BOOKS
ANIMAL DESIGNS

TEEN
COLORING BOOKS
ANIMALS
Black Background

COLORING BOOKS
FOR TEENS
OWLS

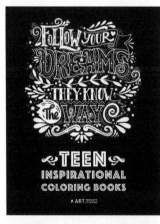

Follow your
DREAMS
THEY KNOW
the WAY

TEEN
INSPIRATIONAL
COLORING BOOKS

TEEN
COLORING BOOKS
ANIMAL DESIGNS
Black Background

DETAILED
COLORING BOOK
FOR TEENAGERS
Animal Designs

Follow
your
HEART

TEEN
COLORING BOOK
INSPIRATIONAL QUOTES

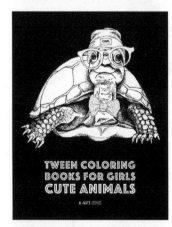

TWEEN COLORING
BOOKS FOR GIRLS
CUTE ANIMALS

ADULT COLORING BOOKS
FOR TEENS
Animal Designs

COLORING BOOKS
FOR TEENS
CAT & DOG DESIGNS

MANDALA
COLORING BOOK
FOR TEENS
Black Background

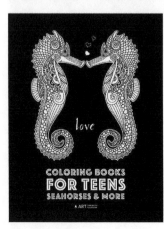

COLORING BOOKS
FOR TEENS
SEAHORSES & MORE

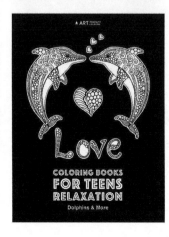

Love
COLORING BOOKS
FOR TEENS
RELAXATION
Dolphins & More

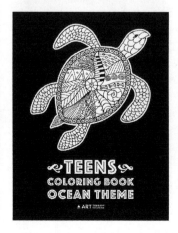

TEENS
COLORING BOOK
OCEAN THEME

COLORING BOOKS
FOR TEENS
SHARKS & MORE

Coloring Books For Teens

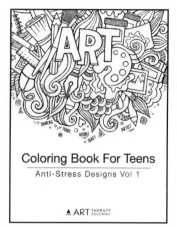

Coloring Book For Teens
Anti-Stress Designs Vol 1

Coloring Book For Teens
Anti-Stress Designs Vol 2

Coloring Book For Teens
Anti-Stress Designs Vol 3

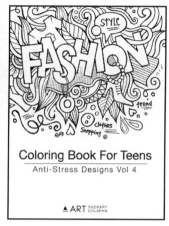

Coloring Book For Teens
Anti-Stress Designs Vol 4

Coloring Book For Teens
Anti-Stress Designs Vol 5

Coloring Book For Teens
Anti-Stress Designs Vol 6

Coloring Book For Teens
Anti-Stress Designs Vol 7

Coloring Book For Teens
Anti-Stress Designs Vol 8

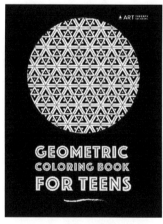

GEOMETRIC COLORING BOOK FOR TEENS

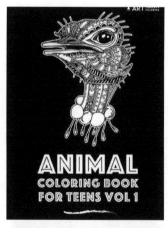

ANIMAL COLORING BOOK FOR TEENS VOL 1

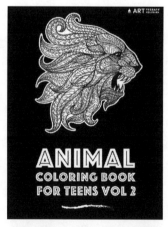

ANIMAL COLORING BOOK FOR TEENS VOL 2

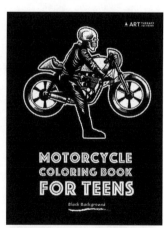

MOTORCYCLE COLORING BOOK FOR TEENS
Black Background

COLORING BOOKS FOR TEENS OCEAN DESIGNS

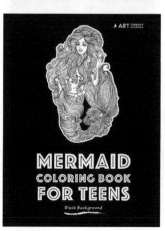

MERMAID COLORING BOOK FOR TEENS
Black Background

SKULL COLORING BOOK FOR TEENS
Black Background

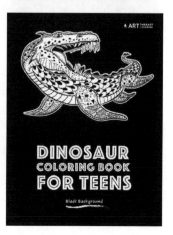

DINOSAUR COLORING BOOK FOR TEENS
Black Background

Butterfly Coloring Book
For Adults: Black Background

Published by:
Art Therapy Coloring
www.arttherapycoloring.com

Images Under License From Shutterstock

ISBN: 978-1-944427-51-1